MY BOOK OF
COLOURS

This book belongs to:

....

....

Illustrated by **Britta Teckentrup**

OW ducklings by the pool

Green

Green

Green

Green

Green

Green

Green
lizard keeping cool

flamingos in the sun

prepare

Blue

walrus by
the sea

Black

cats up
a tree

ed butterflies in the sky

Bro

rabbits leaping high

wn

Colourful

animals everywhere,
on the ground and sea
and in the air.

As the animals look
way up high,
a beautiful

rain

bow

fills the sky!